OXFORD*Playscripts*

•••••••••••••••••••••••••••

cas

Gillian Cross   *adapted by Adrian Flynn*

The*Demon* Headmaster

Oxford University Press

91/4

Oxford University Press, Walton Street, Oxford OX2 6DP

Oxford New York Toronto
Delhi Bombay Calcutta Madras Karachi
Petaling Jaya Singapore Hong Kong Tokyo
Nairobi Dar es Salaam Cape Town
Melbourne Auckland

and associated companies in
Berlin Ibadan

Oxford is a trade mark of Oxford University Press

Original novel **The Demon Headmaster**
© Gillian Cross, published by Oxford University Press, 1982

This adaptation © Adrian Flynn, published by
Oxford University Press, 1990.
Reprinted 1991.
This collection © Oxford University Press, 1990.
Activities in this collection © Bill Lucas.

A CIP catalogue record for this book is available from
the British Library

ISBN 0 19 831270 9

Typeset by Times Graphics

Printed in Great Britain at the University Press, Cambridge

Contents

Characters

At Home

Mr Hunter

Mrs Hunter

Lloyd *their elder son*

Harvey *their younger son*

Dinah Glass *their new foster daughter*

At School

The Demon Headmaster

Rose
Jeff
Simon } *the Prefects*
Sarah
Darryl
Dawn

Ingrid
Mandy } *the 'Normals'*
Ian

Lucy *a pupil*

Julie *a pupil*

Other pupils *sometimes divided into First Circle, Second Circle and Third Circle*

Teachers

On TV

Eddy Hair	*a TV celebrity*
Gloria	*his assistant*
Announcer	
Girl in audience	
Cameraman & Technicians	

Shillingstone School Head and three pupils

Manor School Head, Alec Bates and two other pupils

Others

Miss Wilberforce	*a social worker*

(Many of the parts can be doubled if required)

Scene 1

*The Hunters' home. **Harvey** is lying on the floor reading a magazine. **Lloyd** is pacing up and down.*

Lloyd   A girl!

Harvey doesn't respond.

A girl!

Harvey   *(Not listening)* Yes.

Lloyd   A wretched girl! *(He shakes his brother's shoulder to get his attention.)* Don't you understand what that means?

Harvey   She might be all right.

Lloyd   She'll be completely in the way. We'll even have to take her to school with us.

Harvey   *(Sits up)* You never know. She might be another Normal.

Lloyd   Some chance! There're only five of us in the whole school. She'll be one of them, another goody-goody. Just think. The Headmaster'll have a spy in our own house.

Harvey   It might be interesting. We could spy on her. Find out what's really happening at school.

Lloyd   Don't start that again, Harvey! We don't want to find out. We stay out of trouble.

Harvey   *(Stands up)* Come on, Lloyd. Eddy Hair's starting in a minute. That might cheer you up.

Lloyd   Nothing can cheer *me* up.

Harvey exits.

Why does she have to be a wretched girl!

Lloyd exits.

Scene 2

The Eddy Hair Show. An Announcer comes on.

Announcer   Yes, folks, what you've all been waiting for. Your regular dose of TV craziness. It's the great, the magnificent, 'Eddy Hair Show'!

Audience   *(Live or on tape)* Here's Eddy!

> **Eddy Hair** *leaps onstage and dances round, pretending to be a chimp. Suddenly he straightens up. The* **Announcer** *exits.*

Eddy   Excuse me, I've been going ape today. You know, you must be mad to watch this rubbish and I must be mad to do it . . . That's all right then; we're all mad together. *(He laughs maniacally)* And you're going to see some real trash tonight, folks. There's the Incredible Eddy Hair Challenge, the death-defying high-wire walk with custard and, best of all, the Great School Quiz! Not to forget my exploding socks. Do I really mean exploding socks? I've got you guessing and that's how I like it. Find out after the break.

> *He cartwheels offstage.*

• •

Scene 3

Outside the Hunters' house. **Miss Wilberforce** *enters with* **Dinah,** *who is carrying a large bag.*

Miss Wilberforce   This is the house, Dinah. I'm sure you'll like living here.

Dinah   *(Unenthusiastic)* Yes, Miss Wilberforce.

Miss Wilberforce   They've got two very nice boys, Lloyd and Harvey. I do hope you'll get on together.

Dinah   Yes, Miss Wilberforce.

Miss Wilberforce   It won't be easy getting used to a new family and school but you'll have to try your best.

Dinah	Yes, Miss Wilberforce.
Miss Wilberforce	Are you feeling nervous?
Dinah	No, Miss Wilberforce.
Miss Wilberforce	Hmm . . . Let's meet them.

*She rings or knocks at the front door. **Mr and Mrs Hunter** come onstage. **Mrs Hunter** opens the door.*

Mrs Hunter	How lovely to see you. We've been expecting you. *(She hugs **Dinah**, who stiffens.)*
Mr Hunter	Hello, Dinah.
Dinah	Hello.
Mrs Hunter	Do come in, Miss Wilberforce.
Miss Wilberforce	I won't stay. I'm going to leave Dinah to get to know the whole family. If there are any problems, you know where to ring.
Mrs Hunter	Of course.
Miss Wilberforce	We'll see how she gets on before we make a final decision. I expect she'll be a little bit shy at first.
Dinah	I won't be.
Mr Hunter	At least she knows her own mind.
Miss Wilberforce	Goodbye for now, Dinah.
Dinah	Bye, Miss Wilberforce.
Mr and Mrs Hunter	Bye.

Miss Wilberforce exits.

Mr Hunter	Give me your bag, Dinah.

Dinah	No, it's all right, thank you . . .

Mr Hunter has taken it anyway.

Mr Hunter	My word, it's heavy. What have you got in it? Bricks?
Dinah	Books, actually.
Mr Hunter	What ever does a young girl want with a load of old books?
Mrs Hunter	Let's go through to the living-room. *(She calls.)* Lloyd, Harvey! Come and meet Dinah.
Lloyd	*(Calling from offstage)* We're watching the Eddy Hair Show.
Mr Hunter	Lloyd!

Mr and Mrs Hunter go with Dinah into the living room. Harvey and Lloyd enter and join them.

Mrs Hunter	Now, boys, this is Dinah, who you've heard so much about. She's becoming part of the family.
Harvey	*(Cheerful)* Hello.
Mrs Hunter	That's Harvey. *(Pretending to whisper)* Chubby and cheerful.
Harvey	Cheek!
Mrs Hunter	And the older one's Lloyd.

Lloyd and Dinah look very unenthusiastically at each other for a moment, then they speak at the same time.

Lloyd and Dinah	Hello.
Mrs Hunter	Now you sit and have a nice chat while I go and get the tea ready. *(She tugs her husband's arm.)* Come on.
Mr Hunter	What?

Mrs Hunter	*(Quietly)* They'll get on better without adults breathing down their necks.
Mr Hunter	Make sure you're polite, boys.

> *Mr and Mrs Hunter exit. Dinah, Lloyd and Harvey are left feeling rather awkward.*

Harvey	Can I get you a sandwich, Dinah?
Dinah	No, thank you.
Lloyd	Or a glass of cola?
Dinah	No, thank you.
Harvey	Or a biscuit?
Dinah	No, thank you.
Lloyd	*(Annoyed)* Is that all you can say? 'No thank you'? Are you a robot or something?
Harvey	Perhaps she's shy.
Lloyd	Are you?
Dinah	No.
Lloyd	Then say something different.
Harvey	*(Kindly)* Tell us about yourself.
Dinah	*(As though she's said it many times before)* My name is Dinah Glass. I'm eleven. My parents died when I was one. Since then I've lived in a children's home.
Lloyd	Suffering crumpets! She is a robot.
Harvey	It can't be easy for her . . . Do you want to ask us anything, Dinah?
Dinah	Tell me about school.

Lloyd	*(To **Harvey**)* I told you. A goody-goody.
Dinah	What's wrong with asking about school?
Lloyd	Nothing's wrong . . .
Harvey	Lloyd . . .
Lloyd	*(Firmly)* Nothing's wrong with school. Only we don't like to talk about it when we're not there.
Dinah	I only wanted to ask . . .
Lloyd	We want a break from school, that's all. We're not going to talk about it.
Dinah	I'll find out for myself tomorrow then.

Mrs Hunter enters.

Mrs Hunter	I do hope you've all been having a nice little chat. I'll show you up to your room now, Dinah.

Dinah and Mrs Hunter exit.

Lloyd	What did I say she'd be like? *(Contemptuous)* Asking about school!
Harvey	We ought to warn her.
Lloyd	She'll be just like all the rest. A spy in our own house!
Harvey	Still, it's only fair to tell her.
Lloyd	She'll find out soon enough what school's like. She'll find out soon enough.

Lloyd and Harvey exit.

Scene 4

*The school playground. The **pupils** enter and march across the stage with military precision. They form three perfect circles.*

First Circle *(Chanting)* Once 21 is 21, Two 21s are 42, Three 21s are 63 . . .

*They continue chanting in mime as we hear the **Second Circle**.*

Second Circle William the First 1066 to 1087, William the Second 1087 to 1100, Henry the First 1100 to 1135 . . .

*They continue chanting in mime as we hear the **Third Circle**.*

Third Circle   The capital of France is Paris, the capital of Spain is Madrid, the capital of Japan is Tokyo . . .

>   *All three **Circles** continue chanting in mime as **Dinah, Lloyd** and **Harvey** enter.*

Harvey   I hope I'm not too late to give out the registers.

Dinah   Why don't you run?

Lloyd   Huh! No one runs at this school . . . If you go in now, Harvey, you might just make it.

>   ***Harvey** exits.*

Dinah   I don't understand why you're so worried about registers.

Lloyd   You soon will.

>   ***Ian** enters.*

Ian   Why's Harvey going to the office?

Lloyd   He's got to give out the registers.

Ian   But it's too late. Rose told Sharon to do them. No one else is allowed in now.

Lloyd   Scarlet sausages! I'd better try and get him out before anyone sees him. *(To **Dinah**)* You stay here.

>   ***Lloyd** and **Ian** exit. **Dinah** shrugs her shoulders and walks up to the **Third Circle**. As she gets close to it, we can hear what it's chanting again.*

Third Circle   The capital of Italy is Rome, the capital of the United States is . . .

Lucy (a girl in the circle)   New York.

Julie (another girl in the circle)   Lucy! That's not right.

The Whole Circle	What is it, Lucy?
Lucy	I'm sorry, I was away yesterday.
The Whole Circle	What is it?
Dinah	*(Whispers to Lucy)* Washington D.C.
Lucy	The capital of the United States is Washington D.C...

The Circle turns and looks accusingly at Dinah, who walks away.

Dinah	*(To herself)* Never be too clever. Never let them know.

Rose and Jeff enter.

Rose	Line – up!
Pupils	Yes, Rose.

The pupils form three perfect lines.

Jeff	Lead – in!

The rows lead in silently. Dinah is at the end of the third row. Rose and Jeff stop her from going in.

Rose	Name?
Dinah	I'm Dinah Glass. I'm new and ...
Jeff	Just answer the question.
Dinah	Honestly! Anyone would think you were a teacher, not a kid.
Rose	All pupils shall obey the prefects. The prefects are the voice of the Headmaster.
Jeff	Arms by your side.
Dinah	Don't be so bossy ...

Rose	*(Calling)* Sarah, Simon!

> *Sarah and Simon enter.*

Arms.

> *Sarah and Simon take hold of Dinah's arms.*

This is a new girl. She must report to the Head. Escort her.

Dinah   Wait a minute.

> *Rose and Jeff exit. Sarah and Simon march Dinah round the stage, while Dawn and Darryl carry a desk and chairs on stage for:*

● ●

Scene 5

> *The Head's Office. Dawn and Darryl exit, as the Head enters, wearing sunglasses. Sarah and Simon knock at the office door.*

Head   Enter.

> *Sarah and Simon take Dinah in.*

Head   Whoever can keep order can rule the world.

Sarah and Simon *(Coming to attention)* Sir!

Head   Is this the new girl?

Dinah   I'm Dinah Glass and I . . .

Head   Please do not speak until asked. *(To prefects)* You may go.

> *Simon and Sarah exit.*

Sit down.

> *Dinah sits down.*

Head	I'm going to give you a test all new pupils do.
Dinah	Haven't you got a report from my old school?
Head	Other peoples' reports are no use to me. Please just do as you are told. Spell 'onomatopoeia'.
Dinah	*(Pretends to find this difficult)* Er . . . O . . . er . . . n . . .
Head	Quickly!
Dinah	*(Flustered)* O . . n . . o . . m . . a . . t . . o . . p . . o . . e . . i . . a .
Head	Correct. *(To himself)* Interesting . . . What are seventeen 34s? Work it out in your head, please.
Dinah	Erm . . .
Head	Quickly!

Dinah	Five hundred and seventy-eight.
Head	Correct. *(To himself)* Very interesting . . . What's the chemical formula for sulphuric acid? Quick.
Dinah	H2 SO . . . *(Very deliberately)* 5.
Head	Incorrect. H2 SO4. You're an intelligent girl.

> **Dinah** *looks worried.*

But careless.

> *She relaxes.*

I wonder if . . . It doesn't matter. We'll find out everything about you in due course. Now you must be feeling tired, Dinah.

Dinah	No.
Head	I think you are. *(He takes off his sunglasses and looks at her.)* It's funny you should be so tired this early in the morning.

> **Dinah** *opens her mouth to contradict him, but can't speak.*

Head	You're so tired, your head feels heavy, your eyes are starting to close. You're so very, very tired . . .

> **Dinah** *falls into a hypnotic trance. The focus switches to:*

• •

Scene 6

> *The Dining Hall.* **Rose** *and* **Jeff** *enter, followed by a neat line of* **pupils** *carrying chairs, which they place carefully. The* **pupils** *do exactly what the* **prefects** *say, except for the* **Normals**, *who are always slightly out of step.*

Rose	Collect tray – now.

Jeff	Collect knife, fork and spoon.
Rose	Collect two sausages.
Jeff	One helping of instant mashed potato.
Rose	And seventeen frozen peas each.
Jeff	Sit down.

*The **Normals** sit some way from the other pupils.*

Rose	Start to eat now.

*All the **pupils** raise their knives and forks, then freeze as the focus switches back to:*

• •

Scene 7

*The Head's office. **Dinah** stretches and yawns as she comes out of trance.*

Dinah	I'm sorry. What did you say?
Head	*(Putting his sunglasses back on)* You've been asleep all morning.
Dinah	I don't understand. I wasn't tired.
Head	Go and have some dinner. After dinner, come to assembly with Class One. Is that understood?
Dinah	Yes, sir.

Dinah leaves the Head's office. She shakes her head disbelievingly.

Why did I fall asleep?

*The **Head** exits. **Dawn** and **Darryl** take the desk and chairs in his office off-stage, as the focus switches to:*

Scene 8

*The Dining Hall. **Dinah** enters and collects her meal. All the **pupils** eat silently and in precisely the same way, except for the **Normals**. **Lloyd,** in particular, is a noisy and messy eater. **Dinah** joins the **Normals**.*

Lloyd	Where've you been all morning?
Dinah	Went to see the Headmaster.

*The **Normals** exchange significant glances.*

Ian	What did you think of him?
Dinah	*(Hypnotically)* He's a marvellous man and this is the best school I've ever been to.
Ingrid	Ah-ha.
Mandy	Quiet, Ingrid.
Dinah	What's wrong?
Lloyd	Nothing.

*The **Normals** start eating again.*

Mandy	*(After a moment)* What do you think of the Headmaster?
Dinah	*(Hypnotically)* He's a marvellous man and this is the best school I've ever been to.
Ingrid	Ah-ha!

*The **Normals** nod at each other.*

Dinah	Tell me what's wrong?
Lloyd	Nothing's wrong for you. You'll fit in beautifully.
Ian	*(Pointing to the other **pupils**)* They all say the same thing about the Head.

Ingrid	I bet he said you're to go to assembly after dinner?
Dinah	Yes. Doesn't everyone go?
Mandy	Everyone but us.
Ian	We get extra work with a prefect watching us.
Lloyd	And not because we're thick.

He stands up.

Dinah	Why?
Lloyd	Don't try and work things out.
Mandy	It's best to stay out of trouble.
Ingrid	Make sure you're not late for assembly.
Lloyd	Come on, or we'll be late for class.

*The other **Normals** stand up and follow Lloyd off.*

Harvey	*(As he leaves)* Good luck.

He exits.

Dinah	What do I need luck for? I don't understand.
Rose	Ready for assembly!
Jeff	Lead out!

*Jeff and Rose lead the other **pupils** out. **Dinah** goes over to **Lucy**, who is the last to leave.*

Dinah	Lucy, what's the Head really like?
Lucy	The Headmaster is a marvellous man and this is the best school I've ever been to. *(Frightened)* Quick, or we'll be late for assembly.

Dinah	What happens at assembly?

Lucy has already gone. *Dinah* follows as *Rose* leads the *Normals* into:

. . . .

Scene 9

A classroom at one side of the acting space.

Rose	Sit – down!

They all sit down.

Open your maths books at page thirty-seven.

Ingrid	I haven't done page thirty-six yet, Rose.
Rose	Ingrid! All pupils should be on page thirty-seven by the third Monday of term. Kindly work in silence.

The ***Normals*** *start to work.* ***Rose*** *reads a book.*

Harvey	*(Whispering)* Lloyd! Lloyd!
Lloyd	Sssh!
Harvey	Lloyd!
Lloyd	*(Whispering also)* What?
Harvey	What do you think they do in assembly?
Lloyd	They say they always watch films.
Harvey	But the lights are never turned out. You can see at the edge of the curtains.
Rose	*(Looks up)* Harvey! Why aren't you working?

Lloyd *and* ***Harvey*** *go back to work.*

Harvey	*(After a moment)* I'm going to have a look.
Lloyd	Rubber ravioli! Don't be stupid.
Rose	Lloyd, Harvey! Will you sit still and work!
Harvey	Can I go to the toilet, Rose? I can't concentrate.
Rose	Really! You should learn not to be so disorganised.
Harvey	Please. I can't wait.
Rose	Very well. You may leave the room for one minute twenty-two seconds precisely.

> ***Harvey** gets up and exits.*

Rose	Everyone else, get on with your work.

> ***Rose** and the **Normals** freeze, while the focus switches to:*

• •

Scene 10

> *The Hall on the other side of the acting space.*

Jeff	*(Calling from offstage)* Lead – in!

> *The **pupils** and **teachers** enter in neat lines.*

Jeff	Sit – down!

> *Everyone sits. **Dinah** hurries in on her own. Everyone stares at her as she finds somewhere to sit.*
> *
> **Harvey** comes to the edge of the Hall and looks in, as though through a window.
> The **Head** enters, still wearing sunglasses. He clicks his fingers at **Jeff**, who stands 'on guard' at the door.*

*The **Head** faces the assembly and takes his sunglasses off.*

Head It's funny you should all be feeling so tired this afternoon. So tired your eyelids are starting to close . . .

*All the **pupils** start to fall asleep.*

Dinah *(To herself)* Hypnotism!

She turns her head away.

Head You're so tired. So very tired. You're asleep.

*The whole assembly is asleep. **Dinah**, realizing the **Head** is looking at her, pretends to be asleep as well.*

When you wake up, you will remember you saw a film about ants. If anyone asks you, you will say, 'It was very interesting. We saw how they build their nests and how they look after their eggs.' If you are asked any more questions, you will say, 'I don't remember.' What was the film about?

Pupils *(Together)* It was a film about ants.

Head *(Walking through the children)* Good. Now what this assembly is really about . . .

*He stops because he has seen **Dinah** turn her head to watch him. She pretends to be asleep again.*

Dinah Glass, open your eyes.

She does so.

Your left arm is completely numb. You can feel nothing. Not even this pin.

*He jabs her with a pin. **Dinah** cries out in pain.*

Head	As I thought. Pretending. Look at me, Dinah.
Dinah	I know what you're doing. Hypnotizing everyone.
Head	And I know what you're doing.
Dinah	What?
Head	You're feeling very sleepy . . .
Dinah	No . . .no!
Head	Very, very sleepy.

He looks deeply into her eyes.

Dinah	*(Drowsy)* I'll remember . . . remember . . .
Head	You'll remember nothing at all.
Dinah	*(Almost asleep)* Remember . . .
Head	Nothing at all. You're asleep.

*Dinah is asleep. The **Head** straightens up relieved. **Harvey** sneezes loudly. The **Head** clicks his fingers at **Jeff**, who looks out in time to see **Harvey** running off.*

Head	*(To Jeff)* Well? Did you see the snooper?
Jeff	Yes, sir.

Everyone in the Hall freezes as the focus switches back to:

• •

Scene 11

*The classroom. **Rose** looks up from her book as **Harvey** enters.*

Rose	You are two minutes and twelve seconds late, Harvey.

Harvey	Sorry, Rose.

*He sits back in his place and whispers to **Lloyd**.*

They weren't watching films. They were sitting like zombies listening to the Head.

Lloyd	What?
Harvey	Honest.
Lloyd	We'll ask Dinah on the way home.
Rose	Harvey! Lloyd!

They look back at their books.
The school bell rings.

Rose	Dismiss!

*The **Normals** and **Rose** exit, as does everyone in the Hall. Only **Harvey**, **Lloyd** and **Dinah** are left onstage as they set out:*

• •

Scene 12   *On the way home.*

Lloyd	*(To **Dinah**)* Hurry up if you want to walk home with us.
Harvey	There's no need to be nasty, Lloyd.
Lloyd	We've got something to ask you.

*   ***Dinah** joins them and they start walking.*

Dinah	What?
Lloyd	What did you do in assembly today?
Dinah	We saw a film.

Lloyd gives *Harvey* a significant look.

Lloyd	Oh yes? What about?
Dinah	It was a film about ants. It was very interesting. We saw how they build their nests and how they look after their eggs.
Lloyd	Huh!
Harvey	What else happened, Dinah?
Dinah	I don't remember.
Lloyd	Did the Head talk to you afterwards?
Dinah	I don't remember.
Lloyd	Well, you're either very thick or a liar!
Dinah	*(Angry)* What do you mean?
Harvey	Sorry, Dinah, but I know you're not telling the truth. You see . . .
Lloyd	Don't tell her anything. Can't you see she's one of them?
Harvey	It's only fair to tell her . . . I sneaked out of class this afternoon and looked into the Hall. There was no screen, no projector, no sign of a film.
Dinah	What did you see?
Harvey	The Head talking and you all repeating it back.
Lloyd	You shouldn't tell her anything. She can't be trusted.

*He exits angrily. **Harvey** starts to follow, rather apologetically.*

Dinah	Harvey, what's wrong with that school?
Harvey	I don't know. No one really knows.
Dinah	Well, what's everyone so afraid of there?

Harvey	You'd find out if you got into trouble.
Lloyd	*(Offstage)* Harvey!

> *Harvey exits. **Dinah** is left looking very puzzled.*

Dinah	Something wrong's going on at that school and I don't know what it is. What's more, I don't like not knowing. Well, Dinah, you're used to working things out, so you'll have to work this out. If the only way to find out more is to get into trouble, then you'll have to make some trouble.

> *She nods her head decisively, then exits, as **Mrs Hunter** enters, mixing something in a mixing bowl as she stands in:*

• •

Scene 13

> *The Hunters' house. **Lloyd** and **Harvey** enter.*

Mrs Hunter	Did you have a good day, boys?
Lloyd	Same as usual.
Mrs Hunter	I don't know why you never have anything good to say about that school. All the other children love it. *(She looks up suspiciously.)* Where's Dinah?
Harvey	She's just coming.
Mrs Hunter	I hope you've been nice to her, boys.

> ***Dinah** enters.*

Mrs Hunter	What did you think of school, dear?
Dinah	I think the Head is a marvellous man and this is the best school I've ever been to.

Mrs Hunter	You see, Dinah loves it.
Lloyd	Huh!
Mrs Hunter	Never mind that old sourpuss, Dinah. Let's go and have some tea and cake.

> *Dinah and Mrs Hunter exit. Harvey is about to follow.*

Lloyd	Sky blue sandwiches, Harvey! We've got better things to do than listen to her singing the school's praises. Let's watch TV.

> *He exits a different way, followed rather reluctantly by Harvey as:*

• •

Scene 14

> *Eddy Hair cartwheels on for the next part of The Eddy Hair Show.*

Audience	Here's Eddy!
Eddy	I'm back and don't you wish I wasn't? I'm here with the outrageous Eddy Hair challenge. I'm offering one hundred pounds to anyone who can slurp down a plate of spaghetti in ten seconds. Who'll take up the challenge?
Girl	*(Runs onstage)* Me, Eddy!
Eddy	What a brave girl. Brave but stupid. Are you ready for the challenge?
Girl	I'm ready, Eddy.
Eddy	Gloria, bring on the spaghetti.

> *Eddy's assistant Gloria comes on with an unopened tin of spaghetti on a plate.*

Girl	You haven't opened the tin. I can't eat that.

Eddy	You should have thought of that earlier. You've got ten seconds from now.
Audience	Ten, nine, eight, seven, six, five . . .

Girl desperately tries chewing the tin.

Audience	. . . Four, three, two, one!
Eddy	Out of time and out of luck, I'm afraid. You couldn't eat the plate of spaghetti, so, Gloria, bring the other plate please.

Gloria comes on with a custard pie.

Girl	Steady, Eddy.
Eddy	Will I do it or won't I? I've got you guessing.

He pushes the custard pie in the Girl's face.

| Eddy | Yes I will. |

> *The **Girl** is led off spluttering. **Gloria** mops up any custard on the floor. Applause from **Audience**.*

| Eddy | She was nice, but crazy to trust me. Too crazy to go on my Great School Quiz. But that's not coming up till later. Bye for now! |

> *He bounds offstage as:*

. . . .

Scene 15

> *Lloyd, Harvey and Dinah enter separately. They are in the Hunters' house. They are all wrapped up in gloves, duffle coats, etc. They mime looking out of three different windows.*

Lloyd	Snow.
Dinah	Snow.
Harvey	Snow! *(Excited)* Don't you love snow, Di?
Dinah	Yeah. We used to have terrific snowball fights at the children's home.
Harvey	Snowball fights? What a brilliant idea.
Dinah	We could have one in the playground when we get to school.
Harvey	Fantastic!
Lloyd	Purple pancakes! Think of the trouble you'd get into.
Dinah	Would I?
Lloyd	Real trouble.

> ***Dinah** looks thoughtful.*

Mrs Hunter	*(Enters, carrying **Harvey**'s scarf)* Aren't you ready yet? Put your scarf on, Harvey. You know the cold's bad for your chest. *(She wraps it round him.)* Off you go.
Lloyd, Dinah and Harvey	Bye!
	*They exit. **Mrs Hunter** exits in a different direction as:*

· ·

Scene 16

	The other **pupils** march onto the playground. **Rose** and **Jeff** enter.
Rose	Line – up!
	The **pupils** form three lines.
Jeff	Lead – in!
	The **pupils** march in, followed by **Jeff** and **Rose**. **Lloyd**, **Dinah** and **Harvey** enter.
Lloyd	Guzzling gooseberries! We're late.
	He and **Harvey** walk quickly across the playground. **Lloyd** goes into the school. **Harvey** looks back and sees that **Dinah** is making snowballs. He hurries back to her.
Harvey	Wow! Are we really going to have a snowball fight?
Dinah	No, Harvey! I don't want you involved.
Harvey	*(Snatching up some snow)* Don't be a spoilsport.
Lloyd	*(Hurrying out of school)* Harvey! What are you up to?
Harvey	We're going to have a snowball fight.

Lloyd	Don't be an idiot! Let her get into trouble if she wants to, but don't get mixed up in it.
Dinah	*(To **Harvey**)* He's right.
Harvey	You're both being rotten. The snow may be gone by tomorrow. I'm going to enjoy it now.

> *He throws a snowball at **Dinah** and one at **Lloyd**.*

Lloyd	Don't be stupid!

> *Rose, Jeff, Sarah and Simon appear.*

Rose	Come here.

> *Dinah, Harvey and Lloyd go to the prefects.*

Jeff	It is forbidden to play in the playgound.
Rose	It is forbidden to create mess.
Sarah	You must be punished.
Simon	In a suitable manner.
Rose	Take off your coats and gloves.

> *Pause. The children don't move.*

Rose	*(More sternly)* Take off your coats and gloves.

> *This time the children obey. **Sarah** collects the coats and gloves.*

Jeff	Simon, fetch the brushes.

> *Simon goes off.*

Lloyd	This is your fault, Dinah.

Harvey	I threw the snowballs.
Rose	There is no need to talk.
Jeff	It is unnecessary.

> *Simon comes out with three brushes which he hands out to **Harvey**, **Lloyd** and **Dinah**.*

Rose	Since you like snow so much, you can sweep up the whole playground.
Jeff	When you've finished, you can make it all into a great pile of snowballs.
Sarah	Aren't we kind?
Harvey	Without our coats and gloves?
Lloyd	You can't do that!
Dinah	Harvey's got a weak chest.
Rose	Silence!
Dinah	What if we say no?
Rose, Jeff, Sarah, and Simon	The prefects are the voice of the Headmaster. They must obeyed.

> *Lloyd and Harvey start to sweep. Dinah looks defiantly at the prefects for a moment, then realizes it won't do any good and also starts to sweep. The **prefects** exit. A wind noise builds as the playground becomes bitterly cold.*
> *Dinah, Harvey and Lloyd sweep briskly, but the cold makes the job increasingly difficult. Harvey stops altogether, he's shivering so much. Dinah gives him a hug to encourage him. When all the snow has been swept into the centre, they start*

*making snowballs. The cold, wet snow
makes this agonising and only a
tremendous effort completes the job.*
***Jeff**, **Rose**, **Sarah**, **Simon**, **Dawn**, and
Darryl* *come out as they finish the job. The
wind noise stops.*
*The **Head** enters and stands unobtrusively
at the edge of the playground.*

Dinah   We've finished.

Rose   *(Smiling)* Not quite.

> *She gives a signal at which the **prefects**
> seize the three children and tip them face
> first into the snow, before standing them
> upright again.*

Dinah   That's enough! I'll tell the Head. He'll punish you.

> *The **prefects** start laughing. **Rose** points to
> the **Head**. **Dinah** hurries over to the
> **Head**.*

Dinah   You're disgusting! Harvey's got a weak chest and this'll make
him ill. I'll tell Mr and Mrs Hunter tonight and you'll be
prosecuted.

> *She exits angrily.*
> ***Jeff** signals **Lloyd** and **Harvey** to go off.
> **Dawn**, **Darryl**, **Simon** and **Sarah** exit
> laughing.*
> *The **Head** calls **Rose** and **Jeff** over to him.*

Head   It seems Miss Glass has a soft spot for Harvey Hunter. That
could be very useful. Arrange a prefects' council for tomorrow.
You're going to put him on trial.

Rose and Jeff   Sir!

> *They exit.*

Head	*(To himself)* And I'll have a word with the girl myself after assembly. *(Smiles unpleasantly)*

He exits as:

. . . .

Scene 17

Mrs Hunter enters the Hunters' house. She's mixing something in a larger bowl than before. A door slams offstage.

Lloyd	*(Offstage)* Mum! Mum!

Lloyd and Harvey burst onstage.

Lloyd	Guess what happened?
Mrs Hunter	World War Three started from the sound of it.
Lloyd	No. Something at school this morning. It was terrible.
Mrs Hunter	Don't start with your silly stories again. You've caused all sorts of trouble like that.
Harvey	This really happened.
Mrs Hunter	What?
Lloyd	Dinah'll tell you. You'll believe her.

Dinah enters.

Mrs Hunter	What's all this fuss about, Dinah? What happened at school?
Dinah	*(Hypnotically)* This morning we all made snowballs and had a snowball fight. The Head made sure we all dressed up warmly and afterwards he gave us drinks of hot blackcurrant. It was super.
Lloyd	What!
Harvey	Dinah!

Mrs Hunter	It sounds lovely.
Lloyd	You liar!
Mrs Hunter	Stop it, Lloyd! It's always the same. You tell lies about the school and I get into trouble when I complain.
Lloyd	She's the one who's lying. *(Pointing at **Dinah**)*
Mrs Hunter	That's enough. You've been horrible to poor Dinah since she came here. This is her home as well as yours, so you'd better get used to it.
Lloyd	But . . .
Mrs Hunter	Not another word.
Lloyd	Come on, Harvey.
Harvey	*(To **Dinah**)* How could you?

***Lloyd** and **Harvey** exit.*

Mrs Hunter	I don't know what's wrong with those boys, I really don't. Thank heavens you don't make a fuss about school.

*She puts her arm round **Dinah** and they exit in a different direction to Lloyd and Harvey as:*

. . . .

Scene 18

A burst of music or drum roll introduces the next section of The Eddy Hair Show.

Audience	Here's Eddy!

***Eddy Hair** leaps onstage, carrying a bucket.*

Eddy	OK, folks, I hope you're not enjoying the show. You're numbskulls if you are. Viewing figures show nearly the whole

country watches this programme. The whole country can't be full of numbskulls, can it? . . . It is? *(Manic laugh)* So, if you've any sense, switch off before you watch me cross this tight-rope, carrying a bucket of custard. Here we go.

> *Drum roll.* **Eddy** *mimes walking across a tight-rope, using the bucket to keep his balance. 'Oohs' and 'Aahs' from* **Audience**. **Eddy** *falls off the rope and 'accidentally' empties the bucket over the audience. It is full of confetti, not custard.*

Eddy   Thought it was going to be real custard? I had you guessing. Next up, we have the Great School Quiz. Make sure you see it.

> *He exits laughing as:*

• •

Scene 19

> *The* **pupils** *march onto the playgound. They give a short military marching display, before breaking into their three* **Circles**.

First Circle   *(Chants)* The past participle of être is été.

> **Circle** *continues chanting in mime.*

Second Circle   The square root of a hundred is ten.

> **Circle** *continues chanting in mime.*

Third Circle   Ten millilitres equals one centilitre.

> **Circle** *continues chanting in mime.* **Lloyd** *and* **Harvey** *enter.*

Lloyd   Remember, we're not going to talk to her again.

Harvey   We're the only people she knows.

Lloyd   Then she shouldn't have been a traitor yesterday.

Harvey	I'm not sure it was her fault.

> *Dinah enters. Lloyd pulls Harvey away
> from her.
> She shrugs her shoulders.
> Rose and Jeff enter.*

Rose	Line – up!

> *The pupils form three rows. Lloyd and
> Harvey join the end of one; Dinah joins
> another.*

Jeff	Lead – in!

> *Dinah's row leads in first, Harvey and
> Lloyd's last. As Harvey is about to go in,
> Rose speaks.*

Rose	Harvey Hunter, stop! You are to attend Prefects' Council.
Harvey	But I haven't done anything.
Jeff	Lloyd Hunter, lead in.
Lloyd	I'm staying with my brother.
Rose	That is not permissible.
Lloyd	People have lawyers in court, so he should have one at the council.

> *Rose and Jeff exchange looks.*

Rose	Very well. But it won't do any good.
Jeff	Follow us.

> *Rose and Jeff lead Harvey and Lloyd
> round the stage to:*

Scene 20

*A classroom. **Simon, Sarah, Darryl** and **Dawn** have brought on a table and chairs. There are six folders on the table. **Rose** and **Jeff** join the other **prefects** as they sit down in precisely the same manner.*

Rose	The proceedings may commence.
Simon	*(Reading the charges)* Harvey Hunter, we are here to deal with your disobedient and disruptive behaviour this week.
Sarah	The Head is most displeased with you.
All the Prefects	Most displeased.
Darryl	The charges are: one, you entered school early on Monday morning, even though you know this is forbidden.
Harvey	The Head told me to do the registers . . .
Rose	Silence!
Sarah	Sharon Mandeville did the registers on Monday.
Lloyd	*(Quietly)* It was a mistake. The Head changed his mind.

Shocked silence.

Rose	The Head never changes his mind.
Dawn	*(Reading the charges)* Two: you left your classroom on Monday to spy on assembly in the Hall . . .
Rose	Having lied that you wanted to go to the toilet.
Harvey	*(Shocked)* How did you find out?
Jeff	Silence!
Simon	*(Reading)* Three: you threw two snowballs in the playground yesterday.
Lloyd	He's already been punished for that.

Rose	The prefects took some immediate action, but now we're acting on behalf of the Head.
Lloyd	Why doesn't the Head ...
Harvey	Don't argue, Lloyd. We can't win.
Rose	I'm glad one of you is sensible.
Jeff	Harvey Hunter, you have behaved very badly.
All the Prefects	Very badly.
Simon	But the Head has decided to be merciful.
Harvey	*(Hopeful)* Has he?
Sarah	*(Hands Harvey a thick wodge of question papers)* You simply have to complete these sums.
Darryl	At home.
Dawn	If you complete them, all will be forgotten.
Rose	If not, the Head will deal with you himself.
The other Prefects	Most severely.
Lloyd	Is that it?
Jeff	For the time being.
Simon	You never know, if you can answer those, you might end up on Eddy Hair's Great School Quiz.

> *All the **prefects** laugh and then exit taking table, chairs and folders.*

Harvey	How did they know about me going into school early and spying on assembly? Only you and I knew about those things.
Lloyd	Exploding eggshells! Dinah knew.

Harvey	She wouldn't have told, would she?
Lloyd	Of course she would. She's on their side.
Harvey	*(Looks at sums)* I can't do these.
Lloyd	*(Takes them)* I'll do them for you. *(He looks at them.)* Blue bananas!
Harvey	Are they hard?
Lloyd	No. They're impossible.
Harvey	*(Terrified)* I'm for it now.
Lloyd	We'll show them to Mum when we get home. Even she'll have to admit there's something peculiar going on.

*They exit as **Mrs Hunter** enters in:*

• •

Scene 21

*The Hunters' house. She is mixing something in a still larger bowl. **Dinah** is sitting next to her, drinking a mug of tea.*

Mrs Hunter	Nice day at school, dear?
Dinah	*(Hypnotically)* Every day at school is a useful and stimulating experience.
Mrs Hunter	I'm glad you like it, dear. I only wish you and the boys got on a bit better. It worries me sometimes.

***Lloyd** and **Harvey** enter.*

Lloyd	Mum, can we have a word with you?
Mrs Hunter	Of course, dear.
Lloyd	In private.

Mrs Hunter	Lloyd, Dinah is part of the family.
Lloyd	You don't understand about her.
Harvey	Don't waste time, Lloyd. *(He shows **Mrs Hunter** the sums.)* Look at these sums the Head gave me, Mum.

> *Mrs Hunter gives Harvey the bowl while she takes the sums. She looks at them, turns them upside down, then turns them back again. She shakes her head.*

Mrs Hunter	I don't really understand this new maths, dear.
Lloyd	But it's not new maths. It's just impossible.
Mrs Hunter	The Head wouldn't be so unreasonable, would he, Dinah?
Dinah	*(Miserably)* The Head is a marvellous man.
Mrs Hunter	You see. Now you have a little think, Harvey, and I'm sure you won't find them so difficult. I'm too busy with this cake to help.

She exits.

Harvey	What can I do? The Head'll punish me himself.

> *He starts to cry. **Lloyd** puts an arm round him.*

Lloyd	It's all her fault.
Dinah	*(Comes over)* Can I see the sums?
Lloyd	Are you going to rub it in?
Dinah	Please show me.
Harvey	*(Gives her the sums tearfully)* There.
Dinah	*(Looks at the sums, then whistles with disbelief)* He really didn't want you to do these! You need spherical geometry . . . tensor calculus . . . even the theory of relativity.

Lloyd	*(Sarcastic)* I suppose you can do them?
Dinah	*(Matter of fact)* Yes. Yes, I can. Have you got a pen?

> *Lloyd* gives her a pen. She starts to write at lightning speed, discarding one sheet of questions after another on the floor. *Harvey* gratefully picks them up, while *Lloyd* looks on disbelievingly. While **Dinah** works, we can hear her muttering very rapidly.

Dinah	The chord of the angle 10 is 0.1743 so . . . if the natural secant . . . then given the probability of a series of whole numbers regressing to the power of x . . . taking the circular function . . . y over z cubed . . . multiply by two million, divide by the cosine, think of the number you first thought of . . . *(She discards the last sheet)* There!

> *Harvey* and *Lloyd* stand staring openmouthed for a moment.

Harvey	All fifty of them?
Dinah	Sorry I was so slow, but one or two of them were quite hard.
Lloyd	How on earth did you do them?
Dinah	I'm clever.
Lloyd	Huh! And modest!
Dinah	I'm not boasting. I really am clever at sums and things.
Lloyd	No one told us.
Dinah	No one knows. The Head nearly found out on the first day, but I think I tricked him.
Harvey	Why don't you want anyone to know?
Dinah	You know how horrid people are if you're brainy.

Harvey	Anyway, you've done all my rotten sums. Hurray!
Lloyd	If you've kept it secret for so long, why have you given it away now?
Dinah	I felt sorry for Harvey.
Lloyd	But we've been horrible to you.
Dinah	*You* have. Harvey's been quite nice.
Lloyd	If you like him, why did you tell on him for going into school early and spying on assembly?
Dinah	I didn't. Someone else must have seen him. Probably one of the prefects.
Lloyd	You lied about the snowballs, though. All that stuff about hot blackcurrant.
Dinah	I know I did. I don't know why. Whenever I open my mouth to talk about the school, words come out without me wanting them to. I know what I really think about the Head, but I can't say it.
Lloyd	I wonder why.
Harvey	Assembly.
Lloyd	What?
Harvey	It's the one place Di goes to, that we don't. And we know you don't really see films there.
Dinah	So what happens there?
Harvey	Try to remember.
Dinah	I can't.
Lloyd	You must.
Harvey	Please remember, Di.

Dinah	*(Trying to)* I can't.
Harvey	Remember . . . remember . . . .
Harvey and Lloyd	Remember . . . remember . . . remember.

> *Dinah is struggling to remember, but can't.*
> *Harvey feels a sneeze coming on.*

Lloyd	Remember . . . remember . . . remember.
Dinah	*(Hypnotically)* Remember . . . remember.
Harvey	At-choo!
Dinah	That's it! I was trying to stay awake; I heard a sneeze, and then I fell asleep.
Lloyd	In assembly?
Dinah	I was hypnotized. The Head hypnotizes everyone in assembly.
Harvey	Why?
Lloyd	To stop us misbehaving.
Harvey	To teach us everything quickly.
Dinah	He's not teaching us how to think. It's like a schoolful of robots.
Harvey	How horrible.
Dinah	He won't let your gang go to assembly because you can't be hypnotized, I guess. Some people can't be.
Lloyd	That's right! I remember him looking into my eyes on my first day and telling me I felt sleepy.
Dinah	What happened?
Lloyd	Nothing. I said, 'I'm fine thanks, sir.'
Harvey	That's what happened to me.

Lloyd	It must be the same for Mandy, Ingrid and Ian.
Dinah	But he can control all the rest of us.
Lloyd	He's just a bully wanting to boss around some kids.
Dinah	I don't think that's it.
Lloyd	What do you mean?
Dinah	If you had an army of people willing to do everything you said, wouldn't you want to use it?
Lloyd	Pink pineapples!
Harvey	Don't you think we should tell her, Lloyd?
Dinah	Tell me what?

> *Lloyd* and *Harvey* look at each other. *They nod their heads.*

Lloyd	About SPLAT.
Dinah	What's SPLAT?

> As *Lloyd* speaks, *Ian*, *Ingrid* and *Mandy* enter, carrying boxes to sit on in:

• •

Scene 22   The shed.

Lloyd	SPLAT is the Society . . .
Harvey	For the Protection of . . .
Mandy	Our lives . . .
Ian	Against . . .
Ingrid	Them.

*Harvey joins the other three sitting on boxes. **Lloyd** stays with **Dinah**.*

Lloyd   We meet in this shed. I chair meetings . . . It's very secret. Come on.

*He leads **Dinah** over to the shed and knocks.*

Mandy   *(Giving a password)* Whoever can keep order can rule the world.

Lloyd   But whoever can bear disorder is truly free.

Mandy   *(Mimes opening door)* Pass, friend.

*Lloyd and **Dinah** enter. **Ian, Mandy** and **Ingrid** look suspiciously at **Dinah**.*

Harvey   Have a box, Di.

Dinah   Thanks.

*Dinah sits down, as does **Lloyd**.*

Mandy   Harvey's told us what you've said about assemblies.

Harvey   The question is, what can we do about it?

Lloyd   Hang on! I'm in the chair and I ask the questions. Now, what can we do about it?

Ingrid   How do we know she isn't one of them sent to spy on us?

Ian   She ought to take an oath.

Lloyd   Hang on! I think Dinah ought to take an oath. Dinah Glass, do you swear to honour the secrecy of SPLAT, to protect its members and never willingly reveal anything about us to any of them?

Dinah   I swear.

*The **members of SPLAT** stand up to clasp their right hands together in the air. **Dinah** joins them. They sit down.*

Lloyd	Right. Now we can begin.
Dinah	We've got to find out why the Head wants the whole school hypnotized.
Lloyd	Hang on . . . We've got to find out why the Head wants the whole school hypnotized.
Mandy	Can't you stay awake in assembly?
Dinah	Impossible. I tried.
Ingrid	Perhaps one of us could try and sneak in.

Ian	No chance. They're on double alert since Harvey tried eavesdropping.

Harvey gives an embarrassed cough.

Mandy	Well, what can we do?
Harvey	It's a pity we can't bug the Hall.
Dinah	That's it. Has anyone got a small cassette recorder?
Mandy	I have.
Dinah	I'll switch it on when the Head starts speaking. We'll find out what he's really planning.
Ian	We'll have to have a vote . . .
Lloyd	Wait a minute! I'm chairing this . . . We'll have to have a vote on it.
Dinah	Why?
Ingrid	We're such a small group, everyone has to agree to everything. We can't afford to argue.
Lloyd	Right. All those in favour of Dinah taking in the recorder.

Ian, Harvey, Mandy and Ingrid raise their hands.

Lloyd	What about you, Dinah?
Dinah	I agree, but what do you think?
Lloyd	I don't know, it might be dangerous . . .
Dinah	I'm the only one who'll be in danger.
Lloyd	I'm not so sure.
Ingrid	Oh, come on.
Mandy	*(Impatient)* Lloyd!

Lloyd	Oh, all right. Agreed.

They all stand up again and make their handshake.

Lloyd	Meeting dismissed.

Ian, Mandy and Ingrid exit. Lloyd draws Harvey to one side.

Lloyd	Isn't that typical of Dinah? She joins our society and then starts deciding what we'll do.
Harvey	I think it's very brave of her.

Harvey joins Dinah and they walk off together.

Lloyd	*(To himself)* What's the point of having a chairman with her around? She's either very brave . . . or very foolish.

He exits as we hear a school bell. Dinah enters.

• •

Scene 23

Outside the School Hall. Dinah is checking a small cassette recorder. Lucy enters behind her. Dinah hurriedly puts the cassette recorder in her pocket and turns round.

Dinah	Oh, it's only you, Lucy.
Lucy	Who did you think it was?
Dinah	The prefects or the Head or someone. We're always being watched in this school. It makes me feel like Winston Smith.
Lucy	Who?
Dinah	Winston Smith. He's a character in a book called *1984.*

Lucy	Funny name for a book.
Dinah	It doesn't matter.
Lucy	Let's get into assembly.

*The **prefects, teachers** and **pupils,** joined by **Dinah** and **Lucy,** enter the Hall in neat rows.*

Rose   Stand – still!

*Everyone stands still. The **Head** enters and walks through the Hall. He faces the assembly and takes off his glasses.*

Head   I'm pleased you've all been working well this morning. But now you're all tired. So very tired that you're falling asleep. Asleep.

Everyone is in a hypnotic trance.

Head   Now move into the groups you were in yesterday, where you will receive further instructions.

*Everyone starts to lead off. **Dinah** still has one hand in her pocket, protecting the recorder. The **Head** sees her.*

Head   Dinah Glass, come here.

***Dinah** obeys.*

Head   You look most disordered. Take your hand out of your pocket.

***Dinah** does so, bringing out recorder as well.*

So, we have a spy, do we? Give me that.

***Dinah** gives him the recorder. He presses a couple of buttons, then puts it back in her pocket.*

Head	That deals with that. And now I'd better deal with you. Wake up, Dinah.
Dinah	*(Comes round dazed)* What's happening?
Head	You must have fallen asleep again. *(He produces the sheets of maths questions.)* Do you recognise these?
Dinah	Those are the sums Harvey had to do.
Head	But you did them.
Dinah	They were too hard for him.
Head	They were meant to be. I set them to see if you would help him. To see if you were bright enough to help. Now he'll be punished for not doing them himself.
Dinah	That's not fair!
Head	Fairness is an illusion designed to create disorder. He will be punished unless . . . unless you decide to co-operate.
Dinah	What do you want me to do?
Head	I'll explain in my office. I've great plans for you, Dinah. Great plans.

He smiles evilly, then exits. **Dinah** *follows reluctantly.*

An interval, if required, would occur here.

. . . .

Scene 24

Ian, Mandy, Ingrid, Harvey and Lloyd enter the shed. They sit on boxes.

Ian	Is she really going to be on The Eddy Hair Show?
Harvey	She's in the Great School Quiz.

Mandy	At our school?
Harvey	Yes.
Ingrid	But why's the Head asked her to be in the team?
Lloyd	It proves she's a goody-goody and not one of us.
Dinah	*(Enters)* Oh does it? Is that all you think it means, Lloyd Hunter? Why do you think the Head's asked Eddy Hair to come here at all?
Ian	Fame for the school, I expect. Everyone in the country watches Eddy Hair.
Dinah	Think about it. The Eddy Hair Show's full of mess and chaos, the last things the Head likes. He must have a reason for inviting him.
Mandy	He's up to something.
Ingrid	Yes.
Harvey	But what?
Lloyd	Well, you didn't have to agree to be in the quiz team.
Dinah	Oh yes I did. The Head knows I did Harvey's sums. It was a trap.
Harvey	What?
Dinah	If I don't go in the team and help win the quiz, you'll be the one who suffers.
Harvey	You are clever enough to win the quiz, aren't you?
Dinah	I expect so, but that's not the point. Why does the Head want us to win?
Ingrid	If we watch the programme carefully tonight, we might get a clue.

Harvey	Yes! We can record it . . .
Lloyd	Hang on! Let the chairman say something. We can record it and you can all come round later to watch. Agreed?
Everyone	Agreed.

> *They all stand up and do their handshake. They exit as:*

• •

Scene 25

> ***Eddy Hair,** with two teams of three **pupils** and their **Head Teachers** come onstage for The Eddy Hair Show on tape. They freeze, as the members of SPLAT – **Lloyd, Harvey, Mandy, Ian, Ingrid** and **Dinah** – come onto the edge of the acting space and sit down.*

Lloyd	I've wound it on to the Great School Quiz.

> *He presses a remote control panel and The Eddy Hair Show comes to life.*

Eddy	Shillingstone and Manor Schools are absolutely equal in tonight's quiz, so this is the decider and it's a real brain-buster. Not that it takes much to bust the brains of these yo-yos. *(He laughs maniacally.)* Are you ready?
Teams	Ready, Eddy.
Eddy	Here goes. 'I want to buy roller skates for my chickens. Twelve per cent of them only have one leg and half the rest refuse to wear roller skates. So how many skates do I need to buy?'

> *The teams start frantically, but silently to work out the answer.*

Mandy	That's impossible. He hasn't said how many chickens he's got.

Dinah   It's the same number of skates as chickens. It works out at one each leg.

Lloyd   Oh shut up! We know you've got a brain the size of the Eiffel Tower.

Ingrid   How did you work it out? I couldn't.

Dinah   You're not trained to think at school, that's why.

> *SPLAT becomes quiet as we focus on the tape. One of the Manor Team is speaking.*

Alec Bates   *(One of the Manor team)* Is it the same as the number of chickens, Eddy?

Eddy   The Boffin's done it! Manor school wins!

> *Cheers from **Audience**.*

Now let's have a word with the Head of the losing team.

> *The **Shillingstone Head** steps forward.*

Your lot were a bit wobbly answering the questions, so here's something wobbly for you. Gloria!

> *Gloria enters with a wobbly jelly, which **Eddy** pushes in the **Shillingstone Head**'s face. The **Head** wipes it off and laughs. **Eddy** laughs. **Gloria** wipes up the fallen jelly.*

Eddy   And now we want the secret of success from the Head of the winning team.

> *The **Manor Head** steps forward.*

You've got one minute to tell us exactly how you've produced a schoolful of geniuses.

Manor Head   *(Looking directly at audience)* The secret of good teaching, everybody, is doughnuts. Give your pupils doughnuts every day, especially the jammy ones . . .

Dinah   Stop it there.

The video stops.

Rewind.

Lloyd   What for?

Dinah   Rewind.

Harvey   Go on, Lloyd.

Lloyd presses the remote control. Eddy and the Manor Head move backwards as though being rewound on a video.

Dinah   Play!

Lloyd presses a button.

Manor Head   The secret of good teaching, everybody, is doughnuts.

Dinah   Further back.

Lloyd rewinds. Eddy and the Manor Head move backwards.

Dinah   Play.

Eddy   You've got one minute to tell us exactly how you've produced a schoolful of geniuses.

Dinah   That's it. You can wind it off now.

Lloyd presses a button and everyone on the video exits at video fast forward speed. Dinah stands up as the acting space becomes:

Scene 26

The Hunters' house

Dinah　　Don't you see?

The others stand up.

Lloyd　　See what?

Dinah　　Our Head could hypnotize the whole country if we win. He gets a whole minute in front of the camera.

Mandy　　Is that long enough?

Dinah　　More than enough. The question is, why?

Lloyd　　Huh! That's obvious. He'll tell everyone in the country to rob a bank or something and send him the money.

Dinah　　I don't think it's money he's after.

Lloyd　　You don't want to admit I'm right for once.

Mandy　　It doesn't matter why he's doing it. The point is, what are we going to do about it?

Ingrid　　Couldn't Dinah just lose the quiz?

Harvey　　Oh no!

Mandy　　Think what the Head would do to Harvey.

Ian　　Well, what can we do?

Dinah　　If only we could stop the show from taking place at all.

Lloyd　　Hang on! I'm in the Chair and . . . and *(pleasantly surprised)* as it happens, I do have some very good ideas for stopping the show altogether.

Dinah　　Really?

Lloyd　　Everyone here : . .

The others form a circle round **Lloyd**.

What we've got to do is this . . .

His voice fades to a whisper. The others make the occasional 'Ooh' and 'Aah'. After a moment, **Ian** *turns out of the circle to face the audience.*

Ian   *(Amazed)* Wow!

Ingrid   Wow!

Harvey   Wow!

Mandy   Wow!

Dinah   Wow – ee!

Lloyd   Everyone agreed?

The Others   Agreed!

They make the handshake.

Lloyd   It's our secret till Eddy Hair comes.

They all exit as **Eddy's Announcer** *and a* **Cameraman** *enter.*

● ●

Scene 27   *The school playground.*

Announcer   This looks like the main entrance to the school. I hope they're ready for the broadcast tonight. Go back and tell the lorries to come in this way.

Ian   *(Running on)* Excuse me! Are you from The Eddy Hair Show?

Announcer   That's right, sonny.

Ian	You mustn't come in this way. It's miles from the Hall. The Head says you're to go the other way.
Announcer	Where's that?
Ian	Did you see some great steel gates further down the road?
Cameraman	Looked like a disused quarry?
Ian	That's it. The staff car park really. You're to go there. Through the gates.
Announcer	Are you sure, sonny?
Ian	Certain. All the lorries must go through the gates.
Announcer	Anything you say. Let's go.

> The **Announcer** and **Cameraman** go off. **Ian** takes a big chain and padlock out of his pocket, smiles and follows them. **Ingrid** and **Mandy** enter.

Mandy	Know what you're doing?
Ingrid	I tell the teachers the Head wants them at the swimming pool while . . .
Mandy	(Producing tin of polish and rag) I make sure the side of the pool is nice and slippy.

> They give a thumbs up sign. **Mandy** goes to one side of the acting area, 'opens' the door to the swimming pool and starts polishing the floor.
> **Ingrid** goes to the other side and knocks at the staffroom door. A **teacher** appears.

Ingrid	Please, Miss, the Head says you've all got to go to the swimming pool straight away.
Teacher	Something to do with Eddy Hair coming?

Ingrid	I expect so, Miss. The Head didn't seem very happy. He said you're to hurry.

Ingrid stands back.

Teacher	*(Calling into staffroom)* Come on everybody. Down to the swimming pool, double quick time. Head says so.

> *Mandy stops polishing and holds open the door to the swimming pool as the **teachers** do a 'knees up' run onstage. When they reach the polished area, they start to slip and slide as if in slow motion. This sequence should be extended for effect, possibly with music in the background. **Teachers** threaten to topple over at every angle, catching hold of each other, perhaps even waltzing around, before they finally tumble offstage. There are great offstage cries and splashes. **Mandy** and **Ingrid** lock the door to the swimming pool and slap hands to indicate a job well done, before exiting hurriedly as:*

. . . .

Scene 28

> *Simon, Sarah, Dawn and Darryl enter, crossing the playground to the prefects' room.*

Simon	Now, I'm to take charge of transport with twenty children to help me.
Darryl	Covering Section C of the Master Plan.
Sarah	And I'm in charge of the Work Camps. With fifty children to help me divide up the population.
Dawn	Thus covering Section F of the Master Plan.

> *Dinah and Lloyd enter as the prefects go off.*

Dinah	What do you think they mean? The Master Plan.
Lloyd	I don't know. Let's just lock them in the prefects' room while we can.
Dinah	But Rose and Jeff aren't in there.
Lloyd	We can't help that.
Dinah	They're the most dangerous.
Lloyd	Stop being so bossy. *(He mimes locking the prefects' room.)* Now let's help the others.

He hurries off.

Dinah	Honestly, that boy!

*She hurries off as **Ian** and **Eddy Hair**
enter from different directions.*

Ian	Mr Hair, Mr Hair! You're going the wrong way.
Eddy	That's the only way to get to the right place.

He carries on walking.

Ian	Wait, Mr Hair!
Eddy	Don't ask me for an autograph. You don't imagine I can write do you?

***Eddy** exits laughing.*

Ian	Oh blast!

He runs off as:

Scene 29

Harvey enters the school basement. He is carrying a torch, looking for something.

Harvey *(To himself)* I don't like it down here. Still, someone's got to cut off the electricity.

Lloyd, Dinah, Mandy and Ingrid enter.

Lloyd Have you found the mains switch yet, Harvey?

Harvey It's here.

Lloyd Then let's put out the lights.

Harvey pulls down an imaginary switch and puts on the torch, which is now the only source of light.

Ingrid Great!

Dinah Now let's take out the fuses.

They start taking out fuses. Ian runs on. Harvey shines the torch on him.

Ian I managed to lock all the lorries up in the old quarry, but I couldn't stop Eddy Hair coming into school. We'll be okay though, won't we?

The Head, flanked by Rose and Jeff, enters behind Ian. Harvey gasps.

Ian What's wrong?

Ian turns to see the Head.

Head Well, well, you have been busy, haven't you? . . . Put the fuses back.

Ingrid No, we won't. You're wicked!

Head *(Beckons offstage)* Come here, children.

> *The other **pupils**, in a hypnotic trance, enter silently and menacingly.*

Ian

We'd better do what he says, or they'll make us do it anyway.

> *They put the fuses back. **Harvey** pulls up the mains switch and the lights come back on.*

Head

Do you think I haven't had you watched? Rose and Jeff have released the teachers and the other prefects already. I didn't know about the quarry though. Give me the keys.

> *Ian reluctantly hands the keys over. The Head gives them to Jeff.*

Tell them to get here as quickly as possible.

> *Jeff exits.*

Dinah

You still won't win. I'll answer all the questions in the quiz wrong and you won't get to hypnotize the whole country.

Head

My, my. So clever to work out my plans. But I think you will co-operate . . . in the end. *(To hypnotized **pupils**)* Children, these are six straw dolls, no longer required . . . Tear them to pieces.

> *In a trance, the **pupils** advance and take hold of **Dinah** and the other **Normals**.*

Dinah

Lucy! Let go! Don't you recognise us?

Ingrid

Let go!

Harvey

Help!

> *Very calmly and almost ritualistically, the **pupils** lift the **Normals** in the air and are about to tear them apart.*

Lloyd

Dinah, do something!

Dinah

All right, I'll do it. Whatever you say.

Head	Stop, children!

*The **pupils** let the **Normals** down.*

Head	I'm so glad you've seen reason. Just in case you change your mind during the quiz, your friends will stay with us. If you break your promise, I only have to say 'Destroy the Dolls' . . . the rest I leave to your imagination.
Lloyd	You may have beaten us, but you're still pathetic, doing all of this for money.
Head	*(Genuinely surprised)* Money? I don't want money. I want something much greater. I want . . . *(breaks off)* We must go to the hall, the programme's due to start.

*The **Head** exits followed by all the **pupils**, who keep close guard on the **Normals** as:*

. . . .

Scene 30

*__Eddy Hair, Gloria,__ the **Announcer**, the **Cameraman** and other technical **crew** enter the School Hall. They position chairs, run out cables, and set up the camera in preparation for the broadcast.*

Eddy	Come on, guys. If we're quick, at least we can do some of the show. They're going crazy at Headquarters. If they're not careful, they'll end up like me.

*The **Head** enters and taps **Eddy** on the shoulder. **Eddy** leaps up in surprise.*

Eddy	Aargh!
Head	I didn't mean to startle you.
Eddy	It's okay . . . I thought you were some horrible monster. *(Looks more closely at the Head)* In fact, I think I was right.

Head	*(Forcing a smile)* I was going to ask if I could bring the children in yet? Time's getting on.
Eddy	By all means, egghead, the more the merrier. *(To crew)* Come on, guys, thirty seconds to transmission.

> *The **Head** leads the **pupils** on. They sit round the edge of the stage, guarding the **Normals**.*
> *The two quiz **Teams** enter. **Lucy**, **Rose** and **Dinah** are on one side, **Alec Bates**, two other **Manor pupils** and their **Head** on the other side. **Eddy** goes offstage.*

Cameraman	About to go on air . . . On air.
Announcer	Yes, folks, it's your regular dose of craziness, the magnificent Eddy Hair Show. And here's . . .

> *He waits for the **pupils** to join in. Silence, until the **Head** waves his hand.*

Pupils	*(Lifelessly)* Here's Eddy.

> ***Eddy** bounces on.*

Eddy	Sorry you've had to wait tonight, people. It was due to circumstances beyond my control. But then, everything's beyond my control. *(He laughs maniacally)* We haven't got time for everything, but we're still able to do the fantastic Eddy Hair challenge. I'm offering one hundred pounds to anyone who can eat one of my super-delicious potato chips. Only one. Who'll accept the challenge?

> *Absolute silence.*

	I'm not proud. Anyone'll do . . . Anyone at all . . . *(desperate)* Please.

> *The **Head** signals **Sarah** to go forward.*

Sarah	*(Stepping forward, still in trance)* I'll do it, Eddy.

Eddy	Don't sound so excited, you brave, but foolish girl. Gloria, bring me the chip.
	Gloria brings on a chip several feet long and gives it to Eddy.
Sarah	*(Lifeless)* I can't eat that, Eddy.
Eddy	Why not? Don't you like my cooking? Bring her the seasoning, that might help.
	Gloria and the Announcer bring on huge salt, pepper and vinegar containers. They sprinkle salt and pepper on the chip.

Sarah	*(Absolutely lifeless)* At-choo.
Eddy	Now are you ready?
Sarah	I can't, Eddy.
Eddy	Then you've failed the Eddy Hair challenge. But I'm still going to give you something. *(He pours some vinegar over her.)* There you are, condiments of the chef!

> **Sarah** *doesn't move a muscle.* **Eddy** *is puzzled.*

Eddy	Thanks for being such a lively competitor.
Sarah	Thank you, Eddy.

> *She goes back. The pepper, salt and vinegar pots are left onstage.*

Eddy And on to the Great School Quiz. We've got last week's winners, the smarty-pants Manor School team against the home team. Wouldn't they look good in a gym – two sets of dumb-bells together. *(Laughs)*

> *No reaction from audience.*

Only time for two questions each team tonight. Manor School, question one. King Zonk of Zoldavia has a hundred children. Ninety per cent of them have curly noses, eighty-five per cent of them are bald, eighty per cent of them have one leg and sixty five per cent lisp. How many bald, one-legged lisping children with curly noses must he have?

> **Alec Bates** *starts calculating furiously.*

Eddy	Come on yo-yos, we haven't got all day.
Alec	Thirty.
Eddy	Well done, brain-box. Over to the home team. Your question is this: every room in my house has as many old women in it as there are rooms altogether. Every old woman knits as many knee-

warmers as there are old women. I share out the knee-warmers among seven of my worst enemies, giving each the same number and as many as possible and I still have more than enough to cover my knees. How many have I got?

> The **Head** gives a low cough. The **pupils** take hold of the **Normals. Dinah** sees this.

Dinah   (*Helplessly*) Six.

Eddy   The right answer . . . You know it's usual for the audience to cheer the home team.

> The **Head** raises his hand. The **pupils** cheer till he drops it, when they stop instantly.

Eddy   Craaazzy! I've never seen children organised like that before. Aren't we lucky that teachers don't run the country or we'd all be organised like robots!

Head   It'd be very much better if the country was properly organised, Mr Hair.

Lloyd   (*Calls*) That's it, Dinah! He wants to run the country.

Announcer   Quiet, please!

> **Dinah** nods her head in agreement to **Lloyd.** The **Head** signals to the **pupils** around **Lloyd,** who take a tighter hold on him.

Eddy   Second question for Manor School. Things are hotting up. I have a certain number, made up entirely of sevens. One seven after another. I can divide it by 199. I want you to give me the last four figures of the answer. But, (*Laughs*) I'm not going to tell you how many sevens are in the number. (*Laughs again*) Bit of a sneaky, peaky question. Come on, Smart Alec, what's the answer?

Alec   I . . . I don't know.

Eddy   And neither do I, but I do know that gives the home team the chance to win, if you get this question right. Here we go! I woke up and found I'd lost my memory. I couldn't even remember what year it was, so I asked a man who was walking past. He told me, "If you multiply my age now by twice my age next birthday, you will get the number of the year we are in." Got it?

Lloyd   *(Calls)* You mustn't, Dinah!

> **Lloyd** *is gagged by the* **pupils.**

Eddy   I know it's a tough one, so you can have a clue for half a mark.

Head   Give her the clue!

Eddy   I'm not quite as old as my cousin, Winston Smith.

Lucy   I know! That was the name of the man in that funny book you told me about, Dinah. 1984.

Eddy   1984 is the right answer! The home team win! And there's just time for their Head to tell us the secret of their success. Step forward, please.

> *The* **Head** *comes forward and removes his glasses.*

Eddy   How do you do it?

Head   *(Looking towards the camera and the audience)* If you look into my eyes, I'll tell you. You must be ready for some sense after the chaos of the show. You want to have everything tidied and organised for you. You are feeling exhausted by the mess. You're feeling very tired and ready to sleep . . .

> *Everyone in the hall falls asleep, except for the* **Normals,** *and* **Dinah,** *who is yawning desperately.*

Head   Your eyelids are growing heavier and all you can hear is my voice, telling you exactly what to do . . .

Harvey   Dinah! The pepper!

*With a superhuman effort, **Dinah** wakes up enough to grab the huge pepperpot and shake it over the **Head**.*

Head   You will do everything I say from now on. You are all to . . . to . . . a . . . a . . . aaa . . . AAA . . . TTT . . . CHOOO!

*As he sneezes, everyone in the hall wakes up. The **Head** looks round in panic.*

Head   Destroy . . . the . . . the . . . d . . . AA . . . TTT . . . CHOOOO!

He is convulsed with sneezes. Everyone starts giggling at him.
***Eddy** steps forward.*

Eddy   Well, that's it for tonight's programme, folks. What a wacky Headmaster! But that's this show for you, always something new. I like to keep you guessing. Byeee!

He exits exuberantly.

Head   *(To **Dinah**)* You fool! You've destroyed this country's chance of being the first properly organised, truly efficient nation in the world. AT – CHOOO!

Dinah   We've saved it from being a miserable place full of scared robots. I'm glad you're beaten.

Head   Only for the moment. I'll be ba . . . ba . . . aa . . . AATTCHHOOO! You'll see, I'll . . . AATTCHHOO! I'll . . . AATTCCHHOOO!

*He exits sneezing, with everyone laughing at him. Everyone exits laughing, clearing the acting space, except for **Dinah** and the **Normals**.*

Mandy   We did it!

*They all cheer and make the handshake. **Mandy**, **Ingrid** and **Ian** go off laughing together.*

Lloyd	That was brilliant!
Dinah	Do you think he'll ever stop sneezing?
Harvey	Serve him right.
Lloyd	But what can we tell Mum and Dad?
Harvey	They'll never believe us.

*They exit as **Mr** and **Mrs Hunter,** together with **Miss Wilberforce,** enter in:*

· ·

Scene 31

The Hunters' house.

They all look worried.

Miss Wilberforce	Are you sure that's what you want?
Mrs Hunter	I think it'd be best.
Mr Hunter	I'm afraid so.

***Dinah, Lloyd** and **Harvey** enter.*

Miss Wilberforce	Hello, Dinah.
Dinah	*(Worried)* Hello, Miss Wilberforce.
Mr Hunter	We've asked Miss Wilberforce to come here because . . . well . . .
Mrs Hunter	We're very happy to have you here, Dinah, but . . .
Mr Hunter	Because of the problems, we think you'd better go back to the children's home.
Lloyd	What problems?
Mrs Hunter	You're always arguing.

Mr Hunter	Never getting on.
Mrs Hunter	*(To Miss Wilberforce)* I blame the boys. They never really wanted her here.
Miss Wilberforce	I'm afraid you'll have to come back, Dinah, if you're not wanted.
Lloyd	Plum-coloured pumpkins! Of course we want Dinah here.
Mr Hunter	What?
Harvey	Please let her stay.
Lloyd	For ever. Adopt her properly.
Mrs Hunter	*(Amazed)* You like her?
Lloyd	She's fantastic . . . Except for being a bit thick, of course.
Miss Wilberforce	What about you, Dinah? Do you want to stay?
Dinah	More than anything. Please let me stay.
Mr Hunter	I never will understand children.
Mrs Hunter	Whatever's happened to make you change your minds?
Dinah, Harvey, and Lloyd	Nothing much.

They make their handshakes, as the adults look on, pleased but puzzled.

Activities

Schools

The school in **The Demon Headmaster** has a headteacher of whom everyone is afraid. There are prefects and they seem to be very powerful.

Talk

Complete these tasks in groups.

Headteachers and their schools

Study these pictures.

Which of these is closest to the school in the play?
Which of them is closest to your own school?

Prefects

What do the prefects do in the play? Make a complete list.
Do you have prefects in your school? Do you think having prefects is a good or bad idea for a school? Explain your reasons.

Rules

Does your school have rules?
If so, how many school rules does it have?
Are there any rules which you think are unfair? Explain.
What do you think the rules for the school in this play were? Copy and complete this list.

1. Pupils must be orderly and well-behaved at all times.

2. Pupils must not speak to teachers unless they are spoken to first.

3.

Punishments

What happens to Dinah, Harvey and Lloyd when they have a snowball fight? Do you think the punishment was fair? What good reasons might there be for not having a snowball fight? List any you can think of.
How would you punish someone who has been having a snowball fight if you were the teacher?

Describe any other punishment given out in the play. Is it fair?
What do you think is the point of a punishment?

Make a list of five offences and the punishments you think would be most effective and fair for each one.

Write

Dinah   What's wrong with asking about school?

Lloyd   Nothing's wrong . . .

Harvey   Lloyd . . .

Lloyd   *(Firmly)* Nothing's wrong with school. Only we don't like to talk about it when we're not there.

Dinah   I only wanted to ask . . .

Lloyd   We want a break from school, that's all. We're not going to talk about it.

Imagine you are Dinah. Write two letters to a friend from your last school.
Letter Number One: At the end of your first day . . . what you thought of the prefects . . . your meeting with the Head . . . the playground and your new family.
Letter Number Two: The night before your school is going on the Eddy Hair Show . . . your thoughts, feelings . . . what you now think of the school.

Think

What is wrong with the school?

Dinah   Something wrong's going on at that school and I don't know what it is.

Make a list of anything that you think is wrong with the school in this play.

Talk

Later in this section Gillian Cross describes some of her own memories about school. She describes how she and other children were made to move piles of bricks around the playground:
"It didn't do us any harm, but it wasn't education. It was mindless, repetitive work."

What do you think education is about?
What do your parents think? What do your friends think? What do your teachers think? (Ask them!)

Television

The story of TV

Only a dream
A hundred years ago, television was only a dream. The telephone had been invented, and scientists began to think about sending pictures by wire. But sending pictures by air waves only became a possibility after radio was invented in 1895.

Invention
No one person invented television. Several different inventions made it possible.

In the mid-1920s, two inventors in different countries produced the first television pictures—Charles Francis Jenkins in the United States and John Logie Baird in Britain.

The first broadcasts
The first regular test broadcasts were put out by the WGY station in New York in 1928. In 1936, the British Broadcasting Corporation opened the world's first regular television service.

Colour television
The first television programmes were in black and white. Baird had produced colour pictures in tests in 1929. But it was not until the 1950s in the USA that the first regular colour television broadcasts began.

Long-distance television
In the 1960s, communications satellites were first used to send television pictures over very long distances. In 1964, pictures from Japan were broadcast live in Europe and the USA. That same year, an American space probe sent close-up pictures of the moon back to earth.

This was the first television apparatus, used by John Logie Baird for a famous demonstration in 1925.

Children's TV

5.05pm Blue Peter
With Yvette Fielding
John Leslie and

Neighbours
Henry's attempts at
domesticity leave a lot to
be desired. Kerry and Hilary
let the feat
they have a
over caged
Madge Bishi

Top of the Pops
Bringing you the latest
countdown in vision and
sound from the Top 40 chart.
ced by Simon Mayo.
director Chris Kempton
-/Director Paul Ciani
TANEOUS BROADCAST.
io 1.

5.10pm Moondial
A drama serial
by Helen Cresswell.
4: The sinister Miss Raven
comes to stay and Sarah's
terrible secret is revealed.
Minty................Siri N(
Sarah..........Helana Avella
Miss Vole/Miss Raven
...............Jacqueline Pearce
Tom............
World.......... 'Tony c.
John

**4.40pm Teenage
Mutant Hero Turtles**
The Rat King kidnaps April.

**Enid Blyton's
The Castle of
Adventure**
SCREENPLAY BY
TED FRANCIS AND
LIONEL AUGUSTUS
SUSAN GEORGE
BRIAN BLESSED
CORRINE RANSOM
GARETH HUNT
ISOBEL BLACK
Lucy-Ann and Dinah
ar
an
Kn
hi

**Rolf's Cartoon
Club**
ROLF HARRIS
In today'
program
in the se
Keay-Bri
animatio
co-ordin
Ashley E
the 'worl
prem

**5.10pm
Blockbusters**
BOB HOLNESS
The general
knowledge game
show in which young
people try to win
exciting travel prizes.

Oh! Mr Toad
A TOAD IN TIME
BY BRIAN TRUEMAN
This week, our hero
achieves the
sible with the
f a barley sugar
Narrated by Ian
chael. Anim-

**11.30am
The ITV Chart
Show**
Another edition of the
great British all-video
chart show, with the
chart action and the
fastest Top 10 on TV,
plus some of the best
new releases. This
week the specialist
chart is Indie. Vintage

Talk

1   What are your favourite television programmes?

2   What do you like about the programmes you watch? Explain.

3   Do you ever watch quiz shows?

4   Have you ever seen a programme like *The Eddy Hair Show?* What was
its name? Describe it as fully as possible. Which television programme
can you think of that is closest to *The Eddy Hair Show?*

Write

TV Survey

How many kinds of TV programme can you think of? (For example quiz show, news, soap opera etc.) Make a list of as many as you can think of.

Draw up a chart with this information on it.

Name of programme	Type	Reason for watching it	Number in class who watch it

Carry out a survey on the members of your class, or, if you can, your year group.

What is the most popular TV programme in your class?

Try your survey on your family.

Quiz Show

Video

In groups, make up your own TV quiz game show.

- Re-read the last part of the play where *The Eddy Hair Show* happens.

- Decide on a name for the person who will ask the questions and on what he or she will be like, e.g. Eddy Hair is mad, acrobatic and pours vinegar and other horrible things over the competitors.

- Decide what kind of quiz it will be e.g. will it be a school quiz as in **The Demon Headmaster** or more like *Blockbusters* or *A Question of Sport?*

- Prepare a good number of questions.

- Decide on some of the people you want to have in your quiz, other than the person asking the questions and the contestants.

- Rehearse your quiz show so that you can perform a 5–10 minute extract.

- If your school has a video camera, record your quiz show and then play it back to the class, or perform it to the rest of the group as a piece of drama.

Research

Find out all you can about the early developments of television.
Find out how many people have televisions.
Find out how many people watch popular programmes like gameshows.
How many people do you think the Demon Headmaster hoped he could speak to if his team won?

Hypnotism

Head

When you wake up, you will remember you saw a film about ants. If anyone asks you, you will say, 'It was very interesting . . .' . . . If you are asked any more questions you will say 'I don't remember.'

Read

The children in this play behave in an unusual way because they have been hypnotized. Study this information about hypnotism.

Hypnotism involves putting a person into a kind of sleep. This is normally done by the **hypnotist** speaking in a very relaxing way, while asking the subject to concentrate on a particular object.

Hypnotism was first used in about 1760 by an Austrian medical student called **Franz Anton Mesmer.** Mesmer made a great name for himself in Paris by curing some of his patients by hypnotism. He said that his methods worked because he was able to influence certain magnetic currents in the body. He called this 'animal magnetism'. Although he seems to have cured some people, his methods did not spread to other doctors.

The words 'hypnotism' and 'hypnotist' were first used by a Scottish doctor called **James Braid** in the 1840s. Thanks to his work and that of other doctors, hypnotism became a respectable subject to investigate and an accepted way of treating some patients.

In France **Jean-Martin Carcot** made a detailed study of hypnotism, and showed how it could be used to treat a number of illnesses. **Sigmund**

A scene in Jean-Martin Carcot's clinic: a female patient is cured by hypnosis.

Freud used hypnotism for a time to help treat those of his patients who were psychologically disturbed. After a while he gave it up in favour of other methods and hypnotism gradually became less common by the early days of this century.

For many years, the most common place to see a hypnotist was on the stage, making an entertainment out of it, but recently hypnotism has been making a comeback in several areas of medicine. The police have also been known to make use of it, in cases where a witness is having trouble in remembering important details of what they have seen.

Hypnotism is now accepted as something that really happens without any magical or mysterious explanation.

It is still also used by some entertainers on stage, as in this advertisement.

PETER BASSON

You won't forget him

MINDREADER ■ COMEDY ■ THE SUPERNATURAL ■ FANTASY
THE ULTIMATE COMEDY HYPNOTIST

There are two important things to know about hypnotism.

- You can't normally be hypnotized unless you want to be!

- You won't do anything under hypnosis that you would not normally do in real life.

Talk

1 Who is hypnotized in **The Demon Headmaster?**

2 Which characters are not affected by the Demon Headmaster?

3 Have you ever been hypnotized? Do you think you would have been able to resist the Demon Headmaster?

4 What does the Demon Headmaster try to get his pupils to do?

5 Do you think the events in **The Demon Headmaster** could happen in real life? Explain your answer!

Write

Imagine you wake up one morning and everyone in the world seems to be acting like robots. They are doing things automatically without any real thought. Only a few people still seem normal.
What has happened?
What is going on?
What do you try and do?
Write a story which explains what is happening.

Research

Find out any ways in which hypnotism can be used to help people.

Drama Ideas

Warm-up ideas

1   SPLAT

SPLAT is the name of the Society that Lloyd, Harvey, Mandy, Ian and Ingrid form against the Demon Headmaster. Each letter is the first letter of a whole word. Look at page 47 in the play to find out what SPLAT stands for and what the gang means by it. Make up your own names like this for something you feel strongly about in your own school.

2   Master or mistress and servant

In pairs, one of you gives all the commands, for example: 'Touch all four walls'; 'Say "bananas" to three different people'; 'Move round the room like a frog.'

The 'servant' must decide whether to obey or refuse each command. If he or she refuses, they automatically become the person giving the orders. The two positions are then reversed so that the master or mistress then has to carry out the command. The game then continues, but always remember that the new servant must carry out at least the first command she or he is given!

3   Dictator and spy

One person leaves the room to be the Spy. While the Spy is gone, someone is chosen to be the Dictator. Everyone has to copy the way the Dictator stands or moves, without obviously staring at her or him. The Spy is brought back and the game begins, with the Dictator trying to make as many changes as possible before the Spy guesses his or her identity.
This activity can be performed with everyone standing in a circle or moving around the room.

Longer Activities

1   Making up an advertisement

In groups, try and sell a new brand of chocolate with magical qualities: it will make whoever eats it very clever and very amusing.
Decide what your product is called, make up a slogan and a jingle or tune to go with it.
Work out an advertisement suitable for TV, act it out and, if possible, record it on video tape.

2 The newcomer

In groups, develop this situation: someone new comes to join a family, perhaps a foster child like Dinah, or a relative who has nowhere else to stay.

Decide what the reason for the newcomer arriving is. Think about the challenges, problems and changes this might cause for everyone involved and how the situation might develop. Prepare and act out one or two key scenes which show how everyone is affected.

3 'I've got you in my power'

In groups, explore this situation: one person has gained a great deal of power over some others, perhaps through fear, blackmail or even hypnotism. He or she could be the school bully or a teacher or a gangland boss, for example. Develop a play which shows why the person wants this power and whether, like the Demon Headmaster, their plans come unstuck.

Decide

- what kind of power the person has

- how he/she uses it

- what situations to choose to show this

- how the other people react.

What the Author Says

The Demon Headwhat?

'Why did you call him the Demon Head*master?*' someone said the other day. 'That's old-fashioned. We talk about Head*teachers* now.'

'So we do,' I said. 'But I couldn't call the book *The Demon Headteacher.*'

'Why not?'

So I started to think about headmasters.

I thought about mine. He was a terrifying man. Once, for weeks and weeks, he made us all carry bricks. The parents were building a swimming pool up behind the school and the bricks had been dumped down by the main gate. So the headmaster made us move them. Backwards and forwards we toiled, like slaves. Through the gates, past the infant building, across the playground and up the slope, with our piles of bricks. *Exactly* three to a pile. No more and no less.

It didn't do us any harm, but it wasn't education. It was mindless, repetitive work.

I remember seeing that headmaster drag a small, shivering boy on to the platform.

'Why are you so small?' he shouted.

(No answer from the shivering boy. What could he say?)

'WHY ARE YOU SO SMALL?'

(No answer.)

'I'll tell you why you're so small!' the headmaster thundered. 'It's because you stay up late WATCHING TELEVISION!'

Did he want us all to be the same height?

That man and that school probably had a lot to do with the Demon Headmaster, but I didn't realize it at first. When I was planning the book, I saw it as a kind of cartoon, with the wicked Head, in his billowing black cloak, threatening crowds of terrified children. I imagined him cracking a whip over their heads and driving them along the corridors: all except the few brave ones who dared to defy him. There was nothing serious about the idea. It was just meant to be funny and exciting.

But when I sat down to write, I realized that I had a problem to solve. How did the Headmaster stop the children telling their parents? How could he terrorize them at school, but send them home saying how wonderful he was? There was only one answer that I could think of:

Hypnotism.

That answer changed the picture in my mind. If the Headmaster could hypnotize his pupils, he didn't need to brandish whips around.

He could be very quiet and controlled, but get them to do exactly what he wanted.

Once I realized that, I understood what the story was really about. It's about power and freedom. The Headmaster is obsessed with controlling things. He doesn't want to *teach*, because that means helping people develop skills and understanding, so that they become independent adults. What he wants is to take over their lives and force them to behave as he wants them to.

He wants to *master* them.

So the book has the right title. And if it is old-fashioned, I am delighted to hear it.

'DOWN WITH HEADMASTERS,' I say. After all, we don't all want to be the same height, do we?

Gillian Cross

Talk

1   Gillian Cross suggests that some people might think that her title –
    The Demon Headmaster – is old-fashioned. What do you think?

2   How many words do you know, like 'headmaster', which tell us the
    gender of the person? Make a list of them.

3   Which of the words on your list have alternatives which don't tell us
    the gender of the person? (For example 'Chairman' has the alternatives
    'Chair' or 'Chairperson'.)

4   Are there any words on your list which don't have alternatives? Why do
    you think this is?

5   The headmaster in the story and in this play wants to control children,
    not teach them. Do you think you are being controlled in your school?
    If so, how? Is 'control' a good thing or a bad thing, or good *and* bad?

6   Gillian Cross says that she imagined a man and not a woman running
    the school in her story. What difference would it have made to the play
    if the head had been female? Explain your answer as fully as you can.

Write

Memories of school
What is strongest memory you have of your school life so far? Has any
teacher ever frightened you? Have you ever had an unhappy experience
at school? Have you ever tried to tackle something in the way that the
SPLAT gang do?

•   Jot down any memories you have.

•   Make a list of any words that you associate with your memories.

•   Choose one memory to write about. What did you learn from it?

•   Do a first draft and then read it out to someone else in your group.

•   Produce your final version.

The Demon Headmaster on Stage

Read

Adrian Flynn, who adapted the play from the original novel, has deliberately written a play that is easy to read and perform. If you are interested in acting out this play, study what he has written about performing it.

The play has been written so that it can be performed . . . almost anywhere – from an ordinary classroom, with a restricted acting space and no sets, right up to a well-equipped school stage, making use of sets, lighting and, if available, video cameras and monitors. The only limitations on staging the play are those of imaginatio 1. The following guidelines may, however, be useful.

However it is staged, the action of the play should be continuous, with no breaks for scene changes.

The playing area is used to represent a variety of locations, with each setting being signalled by dialogue or personal props. The only essential items of set are tables and chairs, which can be taken on and off by actors as they use the acting space.

At some points in the play (for example when Dinah goes to her first assembly and the 'Normals' go to class) two scenes take place side by side. To switch the audience's attention from one to the other, it is only necessary for one scene to freeze while the other starts. If stage lighting is available, this can help to switch the focus.

The Eddy Hair Show, segments of which punctuate the main play, can either occur in the same acting space as everything else or, if there is enough room, have a permanent set in a space of its own. If the play is being performed in a fairly intimate drama studio, it may be possible to show *The Eddy Hair Show* pre-recorded on video.

As for props, while some are essential (like the pepper pot at the end) some, like the meal in the dining-hall, exist in mime only, as do all the doors and windows . . . The more you can mime successfully, the more actively your audience watches the play.

One final word. There is no one *right* way of performing a play.

There's only a way which is right for *your* cast and *your* acting space. The only way to find out if something is going to work is to try it. Good luck!

Adrian Flynn

Designing the Set

Think

Study these two possible designs for the set. Go through the advantages and disadvantages of each one and then design your own.

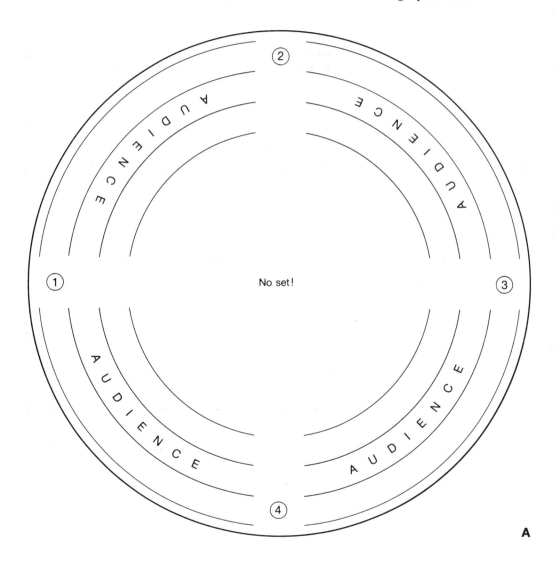

A

Backdrop showing a school

Playground area or
'Eddy Hair Show'

STEPS

Dinah's home

Area set out for assembly

AUDIENCE   AUDIENCE

B

Design

Make a poster advertising a performance of the play that includes a picture of how you see the Demon Headmaster.

Music

Compose some suitable music for
a) the opening of the play
b) the Eddy Hair Show and any other part you think would benefit from some!

Think

How would you
a) make snow on stage for the playground section
b) do the bits which feature the Eddy Hair Show?

Act

In your class, select one section of the play which you would all enjoy acting out. If possible, choose a moment that includes the Demon Headmaster.
Divide your class into groups with the right number of actors, plus one extra person to be the director. (You may decide that one person can play more than one part.)
Before you act it out,

- decide how you are going to play your character.

- if you are playing a speaking part, work out the voice you are going to use, the mood you are in, what sort of person you are.

- if you are the director, give advice to all of your actors about how they might play their parts.

Perform your different versions of this section of the play.

Talk about each version and how they compare. Do you think it would work if you played the Demon Headmaster as a kind, sympathetic figure? Try it!

Acknowledgements

'The Story of Television', p. 79, from *TV and Video* by N.S. Barrett (Franklin Watts, 1985).

The publishers would like to thank the following for permission to reproduce photographs:

Channel 4 Television p. 80; Culver Pictures Inc. p. 83; The Hulton-Deutsch Collection p. 79.
Additional photography by Rob Judges p. 84, and John Walmesley p. 76 (all).

Illustrations are by Martin Chatterton and Alan Marks.

Other plays in this series include:

Across the Barricades   ISBN 0 19 831272 5
    Joan Lingard   adapted by David Ian Neville

Frankenstein   ISBN 0 19 831267 9
    Mary Shelley   adapted by Philip Pullman

Paper Tigers   ISBN 0 19 831268 7
    Steve Barlow and Steve Skidmore

A Question of Courage   ISBN 0 19 831271 7
    Marjorie Darke   adapted by Bill Lucas and Brian Keaney

The Turbulent Term of Tyke Tiler   ISBN 0 19 831269 5
    adapted from her own novel by Gene Kemp

Forthcoming titles include:

The Burston School Strike   ISBN 0 19 831274 1
    Roy Nevitt

Hot Cakes   ISBN 0 19 831273 3
    Adrian Flynn

The Teen Commandments   ISBN 0 19 831275 X
    Kelvin Reynolds

Tigers on the Prowl   ISBN 0 19 831277 6
    Steve Barlow and Steve Skidmore